The Lion of the West

BY JAMES KIRKE PAULDING

JAMES H. HACKETT *as Nimrod Wildfire. A contemporary portrait, reproduced through the courtesy of the Crawford Theatre Collection, Yale University Library*

STANFORD UNIVERSITY PRESS

STANFORD, CALIFORNIA

LONDON: GEOFFREY CUMBERLEGE

OXFORD UNIVERSITY PRESS

The Lion of the West

RETITLED *The Kentuckian,*

or A Trip to New York

A FARCE IN TWO ACTS BY
JAMES KIRKE PAULDING

REVISED BY
JOHN AUGUSTUS STONE AND
WILLIAM BAYLE BERNARD

EDITED AND WITH AN INTRODUCTION BY
JAMES N. TIDWELL

1954

Written in 1830 and revised in 1831 and 1833

First dramatic production, April 1831

First published, December 1954

STANFORD UNIVERSITY PRESS, STANFORD, CALIFORNIA

Published in Great Britain, India, and Pakistan by Geoffrey Cumberlege,
Oxford University Press, London, Bombay, and Karachi

The Baker and Taylor Company, Hillside, New Jersey
Henry M. Snyder & Company, Inc., 440 Fourth Avenue, New York 16
W. S. Hall & Company, 457 Madison Avenue, New York 22

Library of Congress Catalog Card Number: 54-12970

Designed by Adrian Wilson

Contents

Illustrations

(*The decorations are reproduced from wood engravings in*
Bell's A History of British Quadrupeds, *London, 1837.*)

Introduction

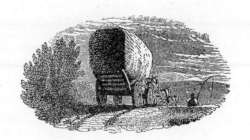

For almost a hundred years scholars of American literature have looked for a copy of *The Lion of the West*, for they recognized its importance in the history of American drama. Even though the play itself was not available, it was known to be the first American comedy to use an uncouth frontiersman as its central character. Before it was produced in 1831, there had been plays about Down-East Yankees, but here was a new, tall-talking, Southwestern type of humor, and here too was reputedly one of the most successful characters in any of the nineteenth-century American plays—Nimrod Wildfire, "The Lion of the West."

The play was known also to be of importance to the student of American history and folklore, for Nimrod Wildfire was felt by the audiences of the 1830's to be a stage caricature of David Crockett, who at that time was cutting a great figure in American politics. Although James K. Paulding, the author, denied in a letter to Crockett that the Congressman from Tennessee was the original of Wildfire and Crockett graciously accepted the denial, the public apparently chose to believe otherwise and continued to identify Wildfire with Crockett. In his *Perley's Reminiscences of Sixty Years in the National Metropolis*, Benjamin Perley Poore relates that at Crockett's request Hackett gave the play in Washington. Crockett was given a front seat to the performance, and upon his entrance the audience, recognizing the famed Colonel, burst into unrestrained cheers and hurrahs. James H. Hackett then appeared on stage in the character of Wildfire and bowed first to the audience and then to Crockett. The redoubtable Davy returned the compliment, to the amusement and gratification of the spectators.

Because of the time which had elapsed since the play had last been produced and because thorough searches of the effects of the author and of the producer had revealed no trace of it, finding the play seemed hopeless when I began my search. Although I had known about the missing drama for many years, my interest did not become active until shortly after I was named assistant editor of the *Dictionary of Political Words and Phrases* in 1947. Paulding's play seemed the sort of material we should read for the *Dictionary*, for in a popular play of its type one might expect to find many politicalisms of the day. My interest led me to talk to Professor Hans Sperber, the editor of the *Dictionary*, about the play and to discuss with him the possibility of finding a manuscript of it. In our conversation Professor Sperber gave me what was the real key to the problem, but I did not recognize it as such at the time. As a consequence I went about the search in a hard, roundabout way.

What was then known about the play can be summarized as follows. In November of 1830 James Kirke Paulding was awarded a prize of three hundred dollars offered by actor-producer James H. Hackett for "an original comedy whereof an American should be the leading character." The judges for the contest were William Cullen Bryant, Fitz-Greene Halleck, and Prosper Wetmore, and the prize-winning play was *The Lion of the West*. Hackett first produced the play at the Park Theatre, New York, on April 25, 1831. Not feeling satisfied with it as a dramatic vehicle, he had John Augustus Stone, author of the

well-known *Metamora*, adapt it. The resulting version
seems to have been produced from the fall of 1831 until
Hackett took his company to England in the spring of
1833. Before its English presentation Hackett again had
the play adapted—this time by William Bayle Bernard,
an English dramatist, who retitled it *The Kentuckian, or
A Trip to New York*, and under that title the play was produced at the Theatre Royal Covent Garden on March 9,
1833. It had a run of several weeks at that London theatre
and a further run of about six weeks at the Haymarket
Theatre; Hackett also produced it in Edinburgh and Dublin before recrossing the Atlantic. Upon his return to the
United States he made the play a regular part of his reper-
tory, and for more than twenty years thereafter the American public could see him in the part of Nimrod Wildfire. So
far as we know, his was the only company to produce the
play and he was the only person to appear as Wildfire.

Despite its success on the stage and its importance in the
history of the American drama, the play disappeared. No
manuscript of it could be found by W. I. Paulding, the
author's son, or by Amos Herold, James K. Paulding's
biographer. Since Hackett had paid Paulding for the original and Stone and Bernard for their revisions, he must
have felt that the play was his property and not the property of any one or all of the authors. If he felt that way
and wished to keep other companies from producing the
play, he may have prevented its publication during his
acting career.

The first blind alley which opened itself to me began at
Patrick Foley's *American Authors*, which lists the play as
having been published in New York in 1831. I could find
no other bibliographies which listed such a work, but I
spent a good deal of time finding out that it had not been
published. Then I set out to learn where and when the
play had been given and what the reviewers had said about

it, hoping to be able to reconstruct the play more completely than had previously been possible and hoping also that some clue to a copy of it might turn up. Along the way I uncovered a story called "A Kentuckian's Account of a Panther Fight," which was seemingly a speech cut from Paulding's original by one of the adapters, and I found further evidence that a supposed speech from the play was really in it, but after three years I seemed no closer to finding the entire play than I had been at the beginning.

Almost in desperation I reviewed everything that I knew of the drama in the hope that some clue was hidden among the seemingly unimportant items—and there was, for it came to me then that I had neglected Professor Sperber's suggestion of years before. The search was simple thereafter, for his idea was that a copy of the play must have been submitted to the Lord Chamberlain's Office to secure approval for producing it at the Theatre Royal Covent Garden in 1833. That copy is the one here published. It had in the meantime been moved to the British Museum and rested there among the Additional Manuscripts, listed as having been written by William Bayle Bernard. By April 1951, I had definitely identified the play through correspondence with the Keeper of Manuscripts for the British Museum.[1]

Finding and identifying the manuscript proved, however, to be merely the first step in getting the play into print. If the manuscript of the play deposited in the Office of the Lord Chamberlain in 1833 was the property of William Bayle Bernard, a copyright might still exist in the work and it could be reproduced only with the consent of the present heirs of Bernard. Under English law a copyright in published dramatic works subsists for fifty years

[1] By an extraordinary coincidence Nils Erik Enkvist, a Finnish scholar, had also discovered the manuscript while preparing his *Caricatures of Americans on the English Stage Prior to 1870* (Helsingfors, 1951).

after the death of the author; in unpublished works the copyright subsists without any limit of time. It was necessary, therefore, either to find legal proof that Bernard claimed no rights in the play or to locate the present heirs of Bernard and get their permission to publish. A search of the Stationer's Hall Register for the period July 20, 1831, to January 26, 1835, disclosed no entry for the play. Bernard's last will and testament was equally unrevealing, for it was written in general terms and might or might not have included the play. The best evidence for Bernard's lack of ownership is the *Catalogue of Dramatic Pieces the Property of the Members of the Dramatic Authors Society or Their Representatives* (London, 1866), which was published by the authors to protect their rights in the plays. In that work Bernard claimed copyright in thirty-six different dramatic pieces, but not in "The Kentuckian, or A Trip to New York." The collection of sufficient evidence to clear the copyright took until September of 1952.

The manuscript of the play is in very good condition, and, although many corrections and deletions were made in it, the entire work is legible except for one word which was marked out too thoroughly—from the context the word seems to have been an expletive. The changes that were made in the manuscript involve principally only two matters: many expletives in the original were taken out, apparently for reasons of taste or morality; and the character called in the original Mrs. Amelia Wollope, author of *Domestic Manners of the Americans*, was apparently felt to be too obvious a reference to Mrs. Frances Trollope, and so her name was changed to Mrs. Luminary, and all direct references to the title of Mrs. Trollope's book and indirect references such as the word *manners* were omitted. The text chosen for reproduction is the A-text—that before the corrections were made. The variant readings of the B-text are given in the Appendix.

Whether William Bayle Bernard made the final corrections included here in the Appendix or rewrote the play before some unknown hand made those corrections, we have no way of knowing. But of one thing we can be sure. If we count the A-text and the B-text as separate versions of the play, there were four versions of it, not three, as scholars have always assumed. Paulding's original drama is summarized in *The Morning Courier and New York Enquirer* for April 27, 1831, and John Augustus Stone's revision is summarized in *The New York Mirror* of October 1, 1831. Neither of these summaries fits the A-text or the B-text. Of the two summaries, the one of Paulding's original is nearer the British Museum copies, for they all have Wildfire attempting to force the British impostor into a duel with rifles, whereas the Stone adaptation has an actual duel between two lovers of the heroine. Stone also developed a lost-daughter theme, which is in none of the other versions; in them Wildfire is a cousin of the heroine.

The play as given here must have been a greater success with the American public than the earlier versions because of the presence in it of Mrs. Amelia Wollope. *The Lion of the West* was, of course, Wildfire's play, but the addition of a caricature of Mrs. Trollope would have increased the enjoyment of any American audience of the time. Frances Trollope, mother of novelist Anthony Trollope, had come to America in 1827 and had set up a department store in Cincinnati. Not only did her business establishment fail, but she herself was hardly accepted into Cincinnati society. She returned to England in 1831 and completed her *Domestic Manners of the Americans*, which was published on March 19, 1832, by Whittaker, Treacher.

Many books by British travelers had condemned many things about the United States and its citizens and had aroused thereby a great deal of American anger, but Mrs.

Trollope's work occasioned an especially violent reaction. Because of it, the name Trollope came to represent in the minds of Americans of the 1830's and 1840's the most unjust criticism of the country by foreign travelers. In fact, her name became a word in our language. In 1864 Henry T. Tuckerman commented in *America and Her Commentators*: "Until recently the sight of a human foot protruding over the gallery of a western theater was hailed with the instant and vociferous challenge, apparently undisputed as authoritative, of 'Trollope,' whereupon the obnoxious member was withdrawn from sight." It seems likely that this epithet grew out of Wildfire's saying that he was most comfortable with his feet out of the window and Mrs. Wollope's remark that she would sketch him thus for her journal. This would argue that the A-text printed herein is the form of the play produced in subsequent engagements throughout the United States; otherwise it is difficult to explain the origin of the word *Trollope* in the sense given by Tuckerman. However, the greater argument for its having been the form produced after 1833 is that a version satirizing Mrs. Trollope would have drawn larger theater audiences.

The American antipathy toward English travelers and particularly toward Mrs. Trollope is only one of the many ways in which the attitudes of that day were not the same as those of today. The reader should remember among many differences that the dramatic taste of 1830 was for melodrama; that the social revolt which gave freedom and stature to the Negro was still thirty years in the future; that the Great Revival was just beginning on the frontier; and that the problem of the protective tariff had just arisen in the tariff law of 1828, popularly called "the tariff of abominations." Hence the usual comic Negro servant is introduced into this play, even though he is used to show that Mrs. Wollope's attitude toward Negroes is worse than the American one. Hence, too, Wildfire can make slighting remarks about Negroes and camp meetings. Hence, finally, Wildfire can make his speech about the tariff—a speech which is amusing because it is completely lacking in relevance, and yet it differs from many of the speeches of the controversy only in being more obviously illogical. Keeping these attitudes of 1830 in mind will enhance the reader's enjoyment of *The Lion of the West*.

Three editorial changes were made in preparing the copy for publication: (1) capitalization was modernized slightly; (2) punctuation, which in the manuscript often consists of dashes or is omitted altogether, was inserted wherever necessary for understanding; and (3) ampersands were written out as *and* except in the abbreviation *&c.*

To Hans Sperber I owe a deep debt of gratitude, not only for his assistance in this project, but also for many other kindnesses and for being the great scholar and great humanitarian he is. I am also profoundly grateful to Miss Kathryn Utz of the Ohio State University English Department for bibliographical references; to Mr. Godfrey Davies of the Huntington Library for his good counsel; and to Mr. A. J. Collins, Keeper of Manuscripts for the British Museum, for his aid in identifying the manuscript. Especial thanks are also due the Library of the Ohio State Archaeological and Historical Society, the Library of the Historical Society of Pennsylvania, the Public Library of Cincinnati, the Crawford Theatre Collection of the Yale University Library, the New York Public Library, the Royal Opera House at Covent Garden, and Mr. Simon Lasica of the Reference Division of the Library of Congress.

JAMES N. TIDWELL

San Diego, California
September 1954

The Lion of the West

Allowd.

En.d

2.? March, 1833.
G.C.

The Kentuckian
or.
A Trip to New York.
A Farce
in
Two Acts

TITLE PAGE *of the manuscript submitted to the Lord Chamberlain for*
permission to produce the play at the Theatre Royal Covent Garden.
(Courtesy of the British Museum.)

Dramatis Personæ

NIMROD WILDFIRE, a Kentuckian

FREEMAN, a New York merchant

PERCIVAL, an English merchant

JENKINS, under the assumed name of Lord Grandby

CÆSAR, a free black waiter at the hotel

  Servants, Visitors, Passengers, &c.

MRS. WOLLOPE,[1] a tourist and speculator

MRS. FREEMAN, the merchant's wife

CAROLINE, her daughter

MARY, Mrs. Wollope's maid

  Waiting woman to Mrs. Freeman

SCENES: The house of Mr. Freeman and the City Hotel, New York.

---

[1] Reference numbers are to B-text variants, which are given in the Appendix.

Dram Pers

Nimrod Wildfire   a Kentuckian.
Freeman   a New York merchant
Percival   an English merchant
Jenkins   under the assumed name of
            Lord Granaby
Cæsar   a Free black waiter at the hotel.

     Servants Visitors Passengers &c

Mrs. Luminary (Wollope)   a Dowager & speculatrix.
Mrs. Freeman   the merchant's wife.
Caroline   her daughter
Mary   Mrs. Luminary's maid
Waiting woman to Mrs. Freeman.

Scene. The house of Mr. Freeman & the City of
      New York.

DRAMATIS PERSONÆ *as given in the manuscript submitted to the Lord Chamberlain for permission to produce the play in England. Note the change of "Mrs. Wollope" to "Mrs. Luminary." (Courtesy of the British Museum.)*

Act One

SCENE 1: *An apartment at Mr. Freeman's. Mr. and Mrs. Freeman discovered at table.*

MRS. FREEMAN. Again, Mr. Freeman, I must say that your views in regard to Caroline are unworthy of a New York merchant. Your ancestors were English and they deem'd it their duty to take their children the grand tour of Europe—

FREEMAN. To make them more contented with their own firesides. Well, my love—admitting that this experiment might be beneficial to my daughter, where could I hope to find a man that would consent to such a roundabout method of possessing her?

MRS. FREEMAN. Are you so blind to the attentions of a certain visitor of ours?

FREEMAN. What, Percival, the English merchant?

MRS. FREEMAN. The English merchant! No, Mr. Freeman—that distinguished member of the English aristocracy who honor'd our child by accompanying her home from the springs.

FREEMAN. Oh! his Lordship.

MRS. FREEMAN. Is not this the man to enlarge her ideas?

FREEMAN. Yes, my love, and to contract her fortune.

MRS. FREEMAN. Would you refuse your consent to a nobleman?

FREEMAN. Mrs. Freeman, this is not the place to discuss the merits of an European institution.[2] In our social system, rectitude and talent confer the only titles. If the result has been the people's happiness,[3] why should I not rather give her to a man whose nobility is in his conduct, not his name?

MRS. FREEMAN. (*aside*) What republican infatuation!

FREEMAN. But come, let us change the conversation. Have you made all your arrangements for our party this evening as Mrs. Wollope visits America to observe our domestic manners?[4] We must permit no remissness to give her an unfavorable impression.

MRS. FREEMAN. Rely upon my pride. But is it not odd that when invited to our country seat to avoid the turmoil of the city, she should decide upon previously proceeding to an hotel?

FREEMAN. This is the duty of a tourist who would justly estimate a people's character—an hotel is a general focus of intelligence.

Enter Servant, with letter.

SERVANT. A letter, Mr. Freeman.

FREEMAN. Ha, from my nephew, Colonel Wildfire.

MRS. FREEMAN. Indeed!

FREEMAN. It is dated Washington, and he is now on the road to New York to spend the summer with us.

MRS. FREEMAN. I regret to hear it.

FREEMAN. Regret!

MRS. FREEMAN. Unless he has corrected that barbarity of which I have heard such descriptions.

FREEMAN. Come, come—consider the circumstances of his education. My sister emigrated to the heart of the Backwoods when they were much less settled than at present. This Nimrod was born a thousand miles from good society, and if his manners are abrupt, they convey a native humour which I think highly entertaining. Listen to his letter. (*Reads.*) "Uncle Peter—Washington, July 1st. Here I am, only two day's journey from New York! The very day I got your coaxing letter I packed up my shirts and some other plunder and set right off a horse-back under high steam. On my way I took a squint at my wild lands along by the Big Muddy and Little Muddy to Bear Grass Creek, and had what I call a rael, roundabout catawampus, clean through the deestrict. If I hadn't I wish I may be *te-to-taciously ex-flunctified.*"

MRS. FREEMAN. There, Mr. Freeman, what do you term that?

FREEMAN. The veritable Kentucky vocabulary. Stay—hear the conclusion. (*Reads.*) "But, uncle, don't forget to tell Aunt Polly that I'm a full team going it on the big figure! And let all the fellers in New York know—I'm half horse, half alligator, a touch of the airth-quake, with a sprinkling of the steamboat! 'If I an't, I wish I may be shot. Heigh! Wake, snakes, June bugs are coming.' Good bye. Yours to the backbone. Nim Wildfire."

MRS. FREEMAN. A pleasing specimen of unrestrained nature.

FREEMAN. Rather eccentric, I confess.

MRS. FREEMAN. Eccentric, Mr. Freeman. You will use any term rather than call obnoxious people by their right names. This man's a savage.

FREEMAN. Mary, you are prejudiced. You will not understand the real character of the Kentuckians. All this whimsical extravagance of speech results from mere exuberance of spirits, and his total ignorance of conventional restraint he overbalances by a heart which would scorn to do a mean or a dishonest action.

MRS. FREEMAN. Well, at least I hope he will not favor us with his company whilst Mrs. Wollope is our guest. What opinion would she form of our national manners from such a man?[5]

FREEMAN. The only just one—that this, like every other, country has its spots where refinement has not entered. She will have too much good sense to consider my wild nephew a specimen of American gentility.

Enter Servant.

SERVANT. Mr. Percival, Mr. Freeman.

FREEMAN. Shew him in!

Enter Percival.

PERCIVAL. Mr. and Mrs. Freeman, I am your most obedient—permit me, madam, to hope— (*Advancing to her.*)

MRS. FREEMAN. (*drawing back*) Ahem—Mr. Percival, will you excuse me? I have some directions to give my servant. (*Exit.*)

PERCIVAL. My friend, pardon me if I'm wrong, but within these last few days I have observed a change in Mrs. Freeman's manner—an alteration so mark'd, I am convinced I have given her some cause—

FREEMAN. Poh, poh—one may see you know nothing of matrimony. If you could explain all the phenomena in a lady's deportment, husbands would be much obliged to you to provide them with an almanac.

PERCIVAL. I should like to set my mind at rest.

FREEMAN. Well, you can do that tonight. You are coming to our party?

PERCIVAL. I have not been invited.

FREEMAN. No? Your distinguished countryman is coming. (Ha! I see a design here. Mrs. Freeman is anxious to secure my little Carry to her favorite.) Percival, you must come tonight. I believe it is my fault you were not apprized of it.

PERCIVAL. Then I'll step home to make some preparation.

WILDFIRE. (*without*) Hello! Wake, snakes—June bugs are cummin! Heigh!

FREEMAN. Ah, arrived already! I must introduce you to my nephew, Colonel Wildfire.

PERCIVAL. Colonel Wildfire—of the army?

FREEMAN. Oh, no — of the militia. Our army in America in time of peace [is] a mere garrison. On your return to England you may rank him next to the wonders of Niagara. He's a human cataract from Kentucky!

Enter Wildfire.

WILDFIRE. Well, uncle, here I am—going it on the big figure—a full team.

FREEMAN. Why, Nimrod, you have reached us nearly as soon as your letter. I'm glad to see you. Let me introduce you to my friend Mr. Percival, a gentleman from England.

WILDFIRE. What, a rale full-blooded John Bull? Stranger, there's my hand. Let me give you a cordial alligator grip.

PERCIVAL. I have no doubt it's a correct imitation.

FREEMAN. Well, nephew, how have you been?

WILDFIRE. Oh, fair to middling—only had a little sprinkling of fever and ague.

FREEMAN. Fever and ague?

WILDFIRE. Yes, I was chuckle head enough to go down the Mississippi fishing for lawyers one day.

FREEMAN. Lawyers! I've found them more apt to catch than to be caught.

WILDFIRE. Why, look here. I call catfish lawyers— 'case you see they're all head, and they're head all mouth.

FREEMAN. Well, did they come to your bait, or lawyer-like, were they too deep for you?

WILDFIRE. Why, I'll tell you. I was fishing for lawyers, and knowing what whappers some on um are, I tied my line in a hard knot right around my middle— for fear the devils might twitch it out of my hands afore I know'd it.

FREEMAN. A good legal precaution.

WILDFIRE. Well, what do you think if a varmint as big as an alligator didn't lay hold and jerk me plump head foremost into the river—I wish I may be stuck into a split log for a wedge! There was I twisted about like a chip in a whirlpool! Well, how to get away from the varmint I was sort of "jubus," when all of a sudden, I grabb'd him by the gills and we had a fight—he pulled and flounced—I held fast and swore at him! Aha, says I, you may be a screamer, but perhaps I'm a horse! The catfish roll'd his eyes clean round till he squinted—when snap went the line, crack went his gills, and off he bounced like a wild Ingen.

FREEMAN. You perceive the humour of my nephew's character—the Kentuckian is our national Gascon.

PERCIVAL. An amusing original!

WILDFIRE. Well, uncle, how are the women—how's Aunt and how's cousin Carry? You writ me she's going it on the big figure, in the Edication line—understands Trignometry and Metyfustian and all that. Why, I say, she must be a sneezer!

FREEMAN. You shall judge of her accomplishments when you see her.

WILDFIRE. So, stranger, you're a traveller, eh? Mean to take a squint, I spose, at old Kaintuck—she's the cream of these United States. When I go back there, I'll take you with me. It's just a leetel ride—only a thousand mile.

PERCIVAL. A little ride—well, sir, perhaps I shall undertake it some leisure afternoon.

FREEMAN. But before you leave us, you expect to be returned to Congress, Nimrod. What will be your sentiments upon this Tariff question?

First Night of The Kentuckian.

THEATRE ROYAL, COVENT GARDEN.

This Evening, SATURDAY, March 9, 1833,

Will be performed, A NEW FARCE, called The

Kentuckian;

Or, A Trip to New York.

Col. Nimrod Wildfire, (a Kentuckian) Mr. HACKETT,
(Performed by him with universal applause throughout the United States of America.)
Freeman, (a New York Merchant) Mr. F. MATTHEWS,
Percival, (an English Merchant) Mr. DURUSET,
Jenkins, (under the assumed name of Lord Granby) Mr. FORESTER,
Cæsar, (a Free Black Waiter at the Hotel) Mr. TURNOUR,
Tradesman, Mr PAYNE, Countryman, Mr ADDISON, Servant, Mr HEATH
Mrs. Luminary (a Tourist and Speculator) Mrs. GIBBS,
Mrs. Freeman, Mrs. VINING, Caroline, Miss LEE,
Mary, Mrs. DALY, Waiting Woman, Mrs. BROWN

After which, (35th time), the Drama of

NELL GWYNNE

The Scenery painted by Mr. GRIEVE, Mr. T. GRIEVE, Mr. W. GRIEVE, and assistants.

King Charles the Second, Mr. JONES, Sir C. Barkeley, Mr. FORESTER
Charles Hart, } Managers of the King's Theatre, { Mr. DURUSET,
Major Mohun, } Drury-Lane. 1667. { Mr. PERKINS,
Betterton (Manager of the Duke's Theatre, Lincoln's-Inn) Mr. DIDDEAR
Joe Haines (late of Drury-Lane) Mr. MEADOWS,
Counsellor Crowsfoot, Mr. BLANCHARD, Stockfish, Mr. F. MATTHEWS
Nell Gwynne, Miss TAYLOR,
Orange Moll, Mr. KEELEY Mrs. Snowdrop, Mrs. DALY.

Scenery painted for this Piece——
EXTERIOR OF DRURY LANE THEATRE in the TIME OF CHARLES II.
LOBBY LEADING TO THE PIT OF DRURY-LANE THEATRE.
INTERIOR OF THE MITRE TAVERN.
PROSCENIUM, AND ROYAL BOX AT DRURY LANE.
Preparatory to " The Prologue by Mrs. Ellen Gwynne, in a broad-brimmed
Hat and Waist Belt.".....(Vide Dryden's Conquest of Granada.)

To conclude with, 14th time, (with new Scenery, Dresses and Decorations) a New DRAMA, in 2 acts called, The

SMUGGLER BOY.

Count de St. Brieux, } otherwise Paul the Smuggler—afterwards { Mr. PERKINS
} under the name of Colonel Valry) {
Vicomte Lepresle, (Commandant) Mr. EGERTON.
Lieutenant (afterwards Major) Auvergne, Mr. DURUSET,
Poltrot Le-Pop, (a Courier, afterwards an Innkeeper) Mr. KEELEY,
Martin, (alias Eau de vie Diable) Mr. G. BENNETT,
Guernsey Bob, Mr. HAINES, Eugene Lepresle, (an Officer, son of the Commandant) Mr. PAYNE
Little Martin, (otherwise Devil's-Skin) Miss POOLE,
Sentinels, Mr. STANLEY and Mr. J. COOPER, Smuggler, Mr. MEARS,
Geniviève, (Countess de St. Brieux, otherwise Madame Valry) Miss TAYLOR,
Clarice, (Sister to St. Brieux) Miss LEE,
Jeannette Piquante, (Waiting-Maid to the Countess, afterwards Madame Le Pop) Mrs. KEELEY
Jacqueline, (Wife of Martin) Mrs. DALY, Pelagie (a Fisherman's Wife) Miss HORTON.

PLACES for the BOXES to be had of Mr. NOTTER, at the Box-Office, Hart-Street, from Ten till Four.

PLAYBILL *advertising the first English performance of "The Kentuckian." Courtesy of the Crawford Theatre Collection, Yale University Library.*

WILDFIRE. The Tariff? What the causes of this row in the south Carolina?[6] Oh, I'm clear for reducing all duties. Only let me gain my election and I'll settle the whole in a single speech.

FREEMAN. A single speech!

WILDFIRE. Yes! Had it in soak these six months— it's rale stall fed. The moment the Tariff Bill comes upon the floor I'll jump upon the table and I shall say to the speaker, Look here, Mr. Cheerman, just stop your steam! Now about these Tariff duties—warn't my father the first man that ever lopp'd a tree in old Kaintuck? warn't he the first to float down Kentucky river with a hogshead of tobacco, when the Ingens stood so thick upon the banks you couldn't see the trees for um? I say, Mr. Cheerman, about this here Tariff—there's no mistake in me; of all the fellers on this side the Alleghany mountains, I can jump higher—squat lower —dive deeper—stay longer under and come out drier! There's no back out in my breed—I go the whole hog. I've got the prettiest sister, fastest horse, and ugliest dog in the deestrict—in short, to sum up all in one word on these here Tariff duties, Mr. Cheerman—I'm a horse!

FREEMAN. An original argument.

PERCIVAL. Not deficient in vigor if in logic. Colonel Wildfire, I shall have the pleasure of seeing you again this evening. (*Exit.*)

WILDFIRE. Uncle, I rather like that feller. I should think he's got some Kentucky blood about him. Well, I must go and look after my trunks and other plunder.

FREEMAN. But don't be absent this evening, Nimrod. We have a party to receive an English lady who intends to make the tour of the states to obtain general information on our domestic manners.[7]

WILDFIRE.   Where is she?

FREEMAN.   By this time, I believe at the City Hotel.

WILDFIRE.   I must go and see her.

FREEMAN.   What for?

WILDFIRE.   I'll give her some general information.

FREEMAN.   But, my dear boy, I've not introduced you.

WILDFIRE.   Then I'll save you the trouble.

FREEMAN.   But there are certain forms you must comply with in this city; you are a stranger to our etiquette.

WILDFIRE.   Who's he?

FREEMAN.   You must have a note to this lady or send up a card.

WILDFIRE.   My card?

FREEMAN.   Perhaps you have no cards.

WILDFIRE.   Yes, but perhaps I've got a pack.

FREEMAN.   But why not delay it till evening? What can you have to say to her?

WILDFIRE.   What! why, that if she wants general information, I'll tell her I'm the boy for all sorts of fun from a camp meeting to a Nigger wedding—heigh! (*Runs off.*)

FREEMAN.   But Colonel! Colonel!

Exit.

SCENE 2 : *Parlor in the City Hotel. Enter Jenkins with a bill.*

JENKINS. (*reads*) "My Lord, the Packet Falmouth is in by which you expected a remittance from England. If you cannot find means to settle your account tomorrow, I shall be under the necessity of desiring you to seek other apartments. Total, one hundred and eighty-five dollars." To John Jenkins, a climax to your career. Five years did you spend your father's patrimony according to the most approved rules of London life, then dropp'd into the travelling companion of a noble friend—until he chose to go his last journey. When to revenge yourself for the loss of your own name, you availed yourself of his, and took wing to America. Here, as the honorable Lord Grandby you have explored every public resort where fashion has begun to set up her academy in search of some rich female who would enable you to escape one prison by opening the doors of another, and your sole hope is the daughter of this merchant Freeman. The mother, I have found, is deeply smitten with a reverence for the aristocracy, and the girl, I believe, is as true a woman as her mother. I am invited there tonight. So tonight I must make a declaration.

CÆSAR. (*without*) Dis way, sar; I hab de honor—

JENKINS. Ah, passengers from the packet. The sound of passengers always makes me uneasy. Ever since the death of her husband, honest Frank Wollope, my speculative sister has talked so often of emigrating to America.[8] It would be very awkward if she chose the present period.

CÆSAR. (*without*) Whose trunk is dis?

SERVANT. Mrs. Wollope's!

JENKINS. What!

CÆSAR. Dis way, marm—I hab de honor—

JENKINS. Eh—no—yes! By all the snakes on the head of Medusa, my fears are realized! What's to be done? If I meet her, I must explain—no, no, I'll run to the Freeman's and there take shelter till I learn her destination. (*Exit.*)

Enter Cæsar, Mrs. Wollope and Mary.

CÆSAR. Dis way, marm. I hab de honor to inform you dis is the City Hotel.

MRS. WOLLOPE. Hum, it seems tolerably furnished —chairs, tables, window curtains—the same as in England. Well, for a land of savages, these are comforts I did not expect. Mary!

MARY. Yes, marm!

MRS. WOLLOPE. Did you see all my things put into the cart? Are you sure you have lost nothing?

MARY. Deary me, I'm afraid, ma'am, I've lost your ridicule.

MRS. WOLLOPE. Ha! Ha! My ridicule in a region of ignorance like this! You need not fear I shall lose my ridicule. Pray, have you such a thing as tea in this house?

CÆSAR. We hab dat honor.

MRS. WOLLOPE. Bring me some, and show my servant to the nearest post office.

CÆSAR. Dis way, young missy. (*Bows Mary out.*)

MRS. WOLLOPE. At length I've reached the scene of my experiment. To ameliorate the barbarism of manners in America has been the ruling wish of my life; my husband, the only obstacle to its fulfillment, by his death has provided me with the means, and the plan I have concerted is founded, I conceive, on a true knowledge of the national character.[9] The root of all the evils of this country is familiarity—where every one is equal, every one is familiar; and this is linked with another barbarism—the women here like those of Turkey are treated as domestic slaves. Now my system is to raise my own sex to its proper dignity, to give them the command and so refine the men.

Enter Cæsar with tea.

CÆSAR. I beg to inform you, marm, dat de tea is made.

MRS. WOLLOPE. China, I declare, and you have got knives and forks here. I thought you always used your fingers. Well, these marks of amelioration give me hopes. Now, my good slave—

CÆSAR. Slave! I hab de honor to inform you dat I am a free gemman of color!

MRS. WOLLOPE. A free gentleman of color? I thought all black people in America were slaves.

CÆSAR. No, marm, only in the suddern states. Here de color'd gemman support trade and help to polish society.

MRS. WOLLOPE. And therefore I suppose you consider yourself my equal. I beg you will display none of your freedom in my presence.

CÆSAR. Marm, do you wish to 'stinguish civil liberty?

MRS. WOLLOPE. Not civil liberty, certainly. It's impertinent liberty I find fault with—familiarity, sir. Remember this, and answer me a few questions respecting the state of manners of this city.[10] (*Bell rings.*) What's that?

CÆSAR. De fuss bell, marm, for dinner.

MRS. WOLLOPE. The first dinner bell. Tho' the hour's in good taste, I think there is something familiar in the summons. Pray, who are the party?

CÆSAR. Gemman in de coffee room who come by de steam boat.

MRS. WOLLOPE. Open the doors. (An opportunity perhaps for my experiment.) (*Cæsar opens door and discovers company.*) What an extraordinary spectacle! Twenty individuals and not one among them with his legs upon the ground! What shocking familiarity with the furniture. No doubt the appearance of a female will restore them to their proper footing. (*Walks past the door unnoticed.*) Now is this inattention wilful? or can't they see me for the smoke? This must be ameliorated. (*Rings bell. Cæsar runs in.*) Inform that person with the paper that I want to speak to him. Now to see if I can get a civil answer to my enquiries.

TRADESMAN. (*coming forward*) Do you wish to see me, madam?

MRS. WOLLOPE. May I ask if you are a resident of New York?

TRADESMAN. No, madam, merely here on business.

MRS. WOLLOPE. But perhaps you can inform me if among your connections you know an English gentleman of the name of Jenkins?

TRADESMAN. Can't say I do, madam.

MRS. WOLLOPE. But possibly your friends in the next room—

TRADESMAN. They are all country people also. However I'll enquire. Does any gentleman present know a Mr. Jenkins? (*They turn.*)

MRS. WOLLOPE. (*aside*) Moved at last. Now for some signs of refinement.

TRADESMAN. This lady is a stranger— (*They rise.*) come over here in search of—

MRS. WOLLOPE. My brother,[11] and I'm sure if any one present possesses the information, he will immediately hasten to—

SERVANT. (*without*) Dinner! dinner! dinner!

They all rush out.

MRS. WOLLOPE. Here's treatment of the sex—desert a lady for a dinner! This must be ameliorated, but they have one thing to excuse them, they are country people.

Re-enter Cæsar with a playing card.

CÆSAR. Gemman at de bar send you his card.

MRS. WOLLOPE. His card — the king of clubs? (*Turns it over and reads.*) Colonel Wildfire. Is he a gentleman?

CÆSAR. Don't know, marm — said he was a horse. (*Exit.*)

MRS. WOLLOPE. A horse! Oh, of the horse—a cavalry officer—the very thing I wished to see. Now for a specimen of an American gentleman.

Enter Wildfire.

WILDFIRE.   Madam, your most obedient.

MRS. WOLLOPE.   Sir.

WILDFIRE.   I believe your name is Mrs. Wollope.

MRS. WOLLOPE.   It is.

WILDFIRE.   Then you know my uncle, Peter Free-man. He tells me you have come among us to take a squint at things in general on this here side of the big pond.

MRS. WOLLOPE.   The big pond! Oh, the Atlantic. That, sir, is my object.

WILDFIRE.   Then I mean to say, madam, on that sub-ject, I can out-talk any fellar in this country—and give him half an hour's start.

MRS. WOLLOPE.   A man of intelligence. Pray be seated.

WILDFIRE.   (*brings forward two chairs, sits on one and as Mrs. Wollope is about to sink into the other, he throws his legs on it*) Now, Mrs. Wollope.

MRS. WOLLOPE.   The soldier tired. Perhaps, sir, you would prefer an arm chair?

WILDFIRE.   No, madam. If it was just after dinner, I should like to put my legs out of [the] winder.

MRS. WOLLOPE.   His legs out of the window—a very cool proceeding certainly. May I offer you a cup of tea?

WILDFIRE.   Much objected to you, madam. I never raise the steam with hot water—always go on the high pressure principle—all whiskey.

MRS. WOLLOPE.   A man of spirit! Are you stationed in New York, sir?

WILDFIRE. Stationed—yes! but don't mean to stop long. Old Kaintuck's the spot. There the world's made upon a large scale.

MRS. WOLLOPE. A region of superior cultivation—in what branch of science do its gentlemen excel?

WILDFIRE. Why, madam, of all the fellers either side the Alleghany hills, I myself can jump higher—squat lower—dive deeper—stay longer under and come out drier.

MRS. WOLLOPE. Here's amelioration! And your ladies, sir?

WILDFIRE. The galls! Oh, they go it on the big figure too—no mistake in them. There's my late sweetheart, Patty Snaggs. At nine year old she shot a bear, and now she can whip her weight in wild cats. There's the skin of one of 'em. (*Takes off his cap.*)

MRS. WOLLOPE. Feminine accomplishments! Doubtless your soil and people correspond.

WILDFIRE. The soil—oh, the soil's so rich you may travel under it.

MRS. WOLLOPE. Travel under ground, sir? I must put this down.

WILDFIRE. Yes, madam, particularly after the spring rains. Look you here now, tother day, I was a horseback paddling away pretty comfortably through Nobottom swamp, when suddenly—I wish I may be currycomb'd to death by 50,000 tom cats, if I didn't see a white hat getting along in mighty considerable style all alone by itself on the top of the mud—so up I rid, and being a bit jubus, I lifted it with the butt end of my whip when a feller sung out from under it, Hallo, stranger, who told you to knock my hat off? Why, says I, what sort of a sample of a white man are you? What's come of the rest of you? Oh, says he, I'm not far off—only in the next county. I'm doing beautifully—got one of the best horses under me that ever burrowed—claws like a mole—no stop in him—but here's a waggon and horses right under me in a mighty bad fix, I reckon, for I heard the driver say a spell ago one of the team was getting a leetel tired.

MRS. WOLLOPE. What a geological novelty.

WILDFIRE. So, says I, you must be a pretty considerable feller on your own, but you had better keep your mouth shut or you'll get your teeth sunburnt. So, says I, good bye, stranger. I wish you a pleasant ride, but I prognosticate afore you get through the next sandbank you'll burst your biler.

MRS. WOLLOPE. This shall be the first well authenticated anecdote in my perusal.

Enter Cæsar.

CÆSAR. I hab de honor to inform you, madam, dat Mr. Freeman's carriage is at a door.

MRS. WOLLOPE. Oh, to take me to his party. Well, after what I have heard and seen I can imagine its refinement.

WILDFIRE. Now, madam, if you are ready, I'll go with you to the tea-squall.

MRS. WOLLOPE. Tea-squall!

WILDFIRE. I say, madam, there's no mistake in you— you're a screamer—you beat our Kentucky widow all holler. She's got but one eye, but that's as cruel as a scalping knife.

MRS. WOLLOPE. How horridly familiar!

WILDFIRE. I say, madam, you and I would make a full team. Hullo! skulk, you black snake! (*Exit Cæsar.*)

MRS. WOLLOPE. What, sir, is a free citizen of America averse to freemen of a different skin?

WILDFIRE. The Niggers! why no, madam, but they're such lazy varmints. I had one once myself, he caught the fever and ague—the fever he kept, but the ague wouldn't stay with him, for he was too lazy to shake!

Exeunt.

SCENE 3: *Drawing room at Mr. Freeman's. Company discovered. Enter Mrs. Freeman and Caroline.*

MRS. FREEMAN. Caroline, you surely have given no encouragement to so plain a person as this Percival, a man of whom you have summ'd up every thing when you say that he is—

CAROLINE. Affable, intelligent and generous.

MRS. FREEMAN. Are these qualities exclusively a merchant's? Has nobility no charm? I'll talk to you no longer. It is my command that you converse this evening solely with his Lordship.

Enter Percival.

PERCIVAL. Dear madam, your husband conveyed to me your wishes that I should spend my last evening in New York beneath your hospitable roof.

MRS. FREEMAN. I could go mad with vexation. So this is Mr. Freeman's design — but I'll devise some method to thwart it the instant his Lordship arrives, and

yet there's another terror to be dreaded—my hopeful
nephew. Should he find his way back from the hotel and
meet my Lord, I fear the latter will be so shocked by
his manners he'll leave the house.

Enter Wildfire.

WILDFIRE. Well, Aunt Polly, I've brought Mrs. Wollope. She's in the next room smoothing her feathers.
Well, what's the fun? I'm ready for anything from a
barbacue to a war dance—heigh!

Enter Freeman.

FREEMAN. Hush—softly, Nimrod, or you'll alarm
the ladies. Colonel Wildfire, my nephew from Kentucky! (*Introduces him to the party and exit.*)

Enter Servant with a tray of ices.

WILDFIRE. Hullo! you rowdy. Here, something to
eat, eh? I'm as hungry as an Ingen in a hard frost. Are
they good? Then I'll take 'em all. (*Takes one, spits
it out instantly.*) Hullo, do you call this a custard?

PERCIVAL. What's the matter, Colonel?

WILDFIRE. I've run foul of a snag. This arn't no custard or a swillybub, but a snowball sweeten'd with lump
sugar. Han't you got nothing better to eat—no bear's
meat or a piece of wild turkey?

PERCIVAL. In the next room, Colonel, you'll find refreshments in abundance.

WILDFIRE. Is there? Then we'll go and take a long
drink together. (*They exit.*)

Enter Mrs. Wollope with Mr. Freeman.

FREEMAN. Give me leave, madam, to introduce you to my friends.

MRS. WOLLOPE. Hum, this place is not so barbarous as I expected—lights, music, ices, Christian looking people with decent clothes on their backs. But I see the aim of this. This has all been concerted to give me a favorable impression of their country.[12]

FREEMAN. I am truly happy, madam, that among other welcomers we shall be able to present to you an illustrious countryman, Lord Grandby.

MRS. WOLLOPE. Lord Grandby—he was my brother's friend.

FREEMAN. Do you know him?

MRS. WOLLOPE. Slightly. The rencontre will indeed afford me much pleasure. A nobleman in a country like this must resemble a diamond in a coal pit. I long to contrast the ameliorated elegance of his manner with the studied efforts of these parvenus.

Enter Lord Grandby.

MRS. FREEMAN. My Lord, permit me the pleasure of making you known to—

MRS. WOLLOPE. (*starting back*) Ah!

JENKINS. Amelia—hush, for heaven's sake![13] Mrs. Wollope, I am delighted at this unexpected pleasure. Encountering an old friend in a strange country gives rise to such strange emotions that— (*To Mrs. Freeman.*) You see, they have taken away her speech.

MRS. WOLLOPE. (*aside*) Is it really you?

JENKINS. All shall be explained. (*Leads her away.*)

Wildfire returns, picking his teeth. Music.

FREEMAN. Colonel, will you join in a quadrille, or take a partner for a waltz?

WILDFIRE. A waltz—what sort of varmint's that—a jig or a war dance? Well, who's afeard? Come, madam, I know you're a screamer.

MRS. WOLLOPE. Excuse me, sir. I never dance. (*Takes out tablets.*)

Music plays.

WILDFIRE. Hullo, stop your steam. That's no dance at all. I want something strong—some music of about 300 horse power. Here, stranger (*To a musician.*), I'll trouble you to play "When Wild War's Deadly Blast Was Blown" and bear pretty considerable hard upon the treble. Oh, don't know it? Then play what you like, only let it go quick on the thunder and lightning principle. (*Music commences a jig. He dances furiously, kisses a girl and exclaims.*) Ain't I a horse! (*Pulls off his coat and recommences dancing. Servant enters with refreshments. Wildfire kicks them over, pulls out dollars.*) Hullo! What's the damage? (*Mr. and Mrs. Freeman importune Wildfire to desist. He throws down dollars. Mrs. Wollope sits sketching in a corner and the curtain falls. End of Act 1st.*)

Act Two

SCENE 1: *Apartment at Mr. Freeman's. Window at back. Mrs. Wollope discovered writing.*

MRS. WOLLOPE. " 'Domestic Manners of the Americans.' Chapter 1st—Arrival in New York and interview with a distinguished gentleman, Mr. Nimrod Wildfire, the Alligator Colonel"—to be illustrated with a sketch of him in his favorite position, rocking in a chair with his legs out of the window.[14] Ha, ha—he little dreams of the celebrity I intend him. The attempt of these people last night to give me a favorable opinion of their condition has only more convinced me of the necessity of my grand ameliorating design—"a national social academy for refinement of manners and elegant exchange for the cultivation of taste."[15]

Enter Mary.

MARY. I beg pardon, ma'am. Do you wish to speak to Colonel Wildfire?

MRS. WOLLOPE. Why do you ask?

MARY. Because he has been walking up and down the garden all the morning whistling at your window.

MRS. WOLLOPE. How horridly familiar! (*Goes to window.*) There he stands, sure enough, his eyes rivetted in this direction. Mary, what does this mean?

41

MARY. Mean, madam? Why, if I may be so bold as to tell you, I think he's fallen in love with you.

MRS. WOLLOPE. In *love* with *me?*

MARY. He has been talking of you all the morning to the servants, and he has paid you such *high* compliments.

MRS. WOLLOPE. Indeed! What has he said of me?

MARY. He says he thinks you could jump over a six barred gate.

MRS. WOLLOPE. The brute! A flattering conquest—the alligator caught. Ha, ha! Can this be possible? I attributed his familiarity last night to any *spirit* but that of *love*, and yet who but that powerful enchanter could tame such a modern centaur?

MARY. Why, everyone is wondering, ma'am, that he should be so *quiet* this morning. Mr. Freeman thinks he's ill. He goes about for all the world like a November wind; one moment he *murmurs*, and the next he *whistles*.

MRS. WOLLOPE. (*returning from window*) This may ameliorate him. What tune has he chosen to pour forth his passion in—a plaintive melody?

MARY. "Yankee Doodle," ma'am. There's a Valentine for you!

MRS. WOLLOPE. A Valentine! An orison! Let me think; can't I turn this discovery to some account? He's a man of *wealth* and *influence* and I know of generosity—he might assist the setting up of my academy. I'll write a note to him and ask him to accompany me to the

ground which I have selected for my building. By thus
flattering his vanity, I shall rivet his chain and lead him as
I please. (*Writes.*) "Dear Sir—I disclosed to you last
night my national project. As I need advice, I wish to
place myself in your hands and shall be most happy to accompany you to the spot which I intend to make my future home in America." There, Mary, carry this to Colonel Wildfire and say I wish an answer. (*Exit Mary.*)
My brother[16] has promised to assist me in this undertak-
ing, and Mr. Freeman is already gone to the city to lay
my prospectus before the merchants. "Academy of refinement at 500 dollars a share"—they can't be so barbarous as to scruple 500 dollars a share! (*Enter Mary.*)
Well, Mary, have you got an answer?

MARY.   The Colonel's writing it, ma'am!

MRS. WOLLOPE.   In his room?

MARY.   No, ma'am, on the ground with a washing tub
turned up for a writing desk—ha, ha!

MRS. WOLLOPE.   (*going to window*) Ha, ha, ha!
There he sits, sure enough, another[17] picturesque position of an American gentleman. Where's my pencil?
I'll sketch him. What a gem for my Journal. (*Takes
pencil &c. and sketches.*) Mary, what did he say on
reading my note?

MARY.   Why, ma'am, he made a note of admiration; he
gave a loud yell and jumped in the air like a man in a
circus.

MRS. WOLLOPE.   Ha, ha! He was so pleased with
my proposal?

MARY.   Oh, yes, he said he'd set about it "right off."

THEATRE.
COLUMBIA STREET.

SECOND and LAST night but ONE of the
engagement of

Mr. Hackett.

First night of the new American PRIZE
COMEDY, in which MR. HACKETT will sustain
his original character of the KENTUCKIAN.

ON THIS EVENING, APRIL 27, 1832,
Will be produced, (first time in this place,)
the new Comedy, to which was awarded the
Prize offered by MR. HACKETT, last spring,
and has been received night after night, in
New York, Boston, Philadelphia and Balti-
more, with such unbounded applause, by the
greatest succession of crowed audiences this
season, called the

LION OF THE WEST.

In 3 acts, written originally by J. K. Paulding, Esq., author of "John Bull in America,"
"Dutchman's Fireside," "Letters from the
South," &c. and subsequently altered and
adapted to stage effect, by J. A. Stone, Esq.
author of "Metamora," &c.

COL. NIMROD WILDFIRE, MR. HACKETT,
[The Kentuckian.]

After which will be performed the admired
farce of the

Honest Thieves.

TAGUE, - - - MR. LUDLOW.

Saturday, last night of MR. HACKETT'S
engagement, when he will appear in two more
of his original and most popular characters.

☞ The public are respectfully notified that
the fixed period of Mr. Hackett's appearance
at the North, precludes the possibility of any
renewal or extension of his engagement in this
City.

Places and Boxes can be secured by applica-
tion at the Theatre from 10 till 12, A. M., and
from 5 till 7, P. M.
Prices of Admission—To the first Tier Boxes
$1,—Pit and 2d Tier 75 cents,—3d Tier 37½
cents.
March 27

NEWSPAPER ADVERTISEMENT *which appeared in the* Cincinnati
Daily Gazette *of April 27, 1832, p. 3, col. 3. Courtesy of the Public
Library of Cincinnati.*

MRS. WOLLOPE. There, I knew this would be good generalship. He'll have my building up before another would have collected the subscriptions.

MARY. And so, ma'am, he has sent for a four horse waggon.

MRS. WOLLOPE. A four horse waggon? Oh, to drive me to the spot—that, I suppose, is Kentucky *ton*.

MARY. But, ma'am, I heard him tell the gardener to run for a clergyman.

MRS. WOLLOPE. A clergyman? (*Knock, L.H.*)

MARY. A clergyman. (*Going to door.*)

MRS. WOLLOPE. Ah, to solemnize the foundation of my academy—better and better. This is doing things, as he says, in a *whirlwind!*

MARY. (*returning*) Here's the answer, ma'am!

MRS. WOLLOPE. (*reads*) "Most ameliorating widow! You say you wish to put yourself into my hands and go home with me to old Kaintuck—it's a match." Mary! "I have ordered a good strong covered waggon for the journey. There's a parson close by who hitches teams quicker than any feller in the country. I'll go fetch him by the collar in less than a flash. In five minutes we two will be hammered into one—and then—" (*Drops letter.*) Gracious Powers!

MARY. Ma'am!

MRS. WOLLOPE. What does the man mean?

MARY. I'm sure I can't tell, ma'am!

MRS. WOLLOPE. Marry me and carry me in a covered waggon to the backwoods! The stupid, ignorant, familiar brute—does he think for a moment I could waste a thought—the supposition is an insult! This must be ameliorated!

MARY.   Yes, ma'am!

MRS. WOLLOPE.   I'll send him a message that will bring him to his senses. (*Sitting down. Cracking of a whip outside.*)

MARY.   (*at window*) La, ma'am!

MRS. WOLLOPE.   Well!

MARY.   As I live and breathe, here comes the covered waggon.

MRS. WOLLOPE.   What? (*Runs to window.*) It is, sure enough. Is he then in earnest? Good heavens,[18] if the passions of this savage are really excited, no power on earth will subdue them. I am not safe. I must send to him and rectify the error instantly. Mary (*Sits and writes.*), you must run with this to Colonel Wildfire.

MARY.   He's not in the garden, ma'am!

MRS. WOLLOPE.   He can't have gone for the clergyman.

MARY.   I'm sure, ma'am, I'm in doubt!

MRS. WOLLOPE.   Don't doubt; run and see.

MARY.   Here comes his man.

Enter Countryman.

COUNTRYMAN.   Colonel sent me up to cord your boxes—

MRS. WOLLOPE.   Cord my boxes, fellow? How dare

your master interpret my letter in this manner. Run after him, and tell him to step here instantly. (*Exit Countryman. She rings a bell. A white servant girl enters.*) Tell Mrs. Freeman I wish to speak to her.

SERVANT. She is gone out, ma'am.

MRS. WOLLOPE. Without my knowing it!

SERVANT. Why, ma'am, you said at breakfast you didn't want to be disturbed.

MRS. WOLLOPE. But you don't mean to say that I am *alone* in this house?

SERVANT. Oh, no, ma'am. There's two of us to wait upon you—me and another Nigger wench. (*Exit.*)

MRS. WOLLOPE. Mary!

MARY. Ma'am?

MRS. WOLLOPE. Do you hear that? I'm betrayed— there's not a soul here that can defend me. This savage will marry me by main force, thrust me into his covered waggon, and then—

MARY. La, ma'am, don't think of it!

MRS. WOLLOPE. I see it plainly—it's a plot of the whole family. I was warned of the total want of probity in these people.[19] This is their gratitude for my desire to ameliorate their manners.[20] Oh, what a fool I was to leave England—safe, civilized England—to fall a sacrifice to pure philanthropy.

MARY. But it isn't too late, ma'am. I'll call out.

MRS. WOLLOPE. Call out! What will our feeble voices avail against the Indian war whoop of a Kentucky hunter and the chorus of a Yankee clergyman? (*Trampling without.*) Ah, the ruffian's coming—help!

Enter Jenkins. Mary goes out.

JENKINS. Amelia.[21]

MRS. WOLLOPE. It's well you've come at last, sir.[22]

JENKINS. My dear sister, what has happened?[23]

MRS. WOLLOPE. This colonel of American horse, this *Kentucky* child of chivalry.

JENKINS. Well?

MRS. WOLLOPE. Pitying the savage's condition, I asked him to subscribe to my academy. He in his ignorance of English interprets this wish—but read, read! (*Gives letter.*)

JENKINS. Ha, ha! An amusing mistake.

MRS. WOLLOPE. Do you call it amusing? Do you know that this man prides himself on his being half an alligator?

JENKINS. Well?

MRS. WOLLOPE. You see he is gone for an expeditious clergyman.

JENKINS. Is that your only danger?

MRS. WOLLOPE. A great deal more.

JENKINS. What?

MRS. WOLLOPE. A covered waggon.

JENKINS. Well, well, if he annoys you, I must frighten him—talk of pistols.

MRS. WOLLOPE. Pistols?

JENKINS. Like all wild animals he is formidable with his claws, but the smell of powder would scare him back to his native woods.

MRS. WOLLOPE. Then, my dear brother,[24] shoot him instantly.

JENKINS. But, Amelia,[25] have you kept your promise —your influence with the merchant about his daughter?

MRS. WOLLOPE. No, but deliver me from this dilemma and I'll do anything.

JENKINS. Here, then, I take my stand. (*Looking from window.*) Eh, by heaven,[26] 'tis Caroline in the garden. This opportunity must not be lost. Amelia,[27] I'll return to you instantly. (*Exit.*)

MRS. WOLLOPE. (*sinking into a chair*) What perils are we exposed to who desert our own firesides to increase the comforts of a thankless world, and yet if I fear the barbarisms of these people, how shall I ever overcome them? I'll look at it less seriously. Stay, it would make a feature in my Journal. Let me see—yes, under this head: "Anecdote of the Alligator Colonel"— "mode of marrying in a whirlwind." Ha, ha, ha![28]

WILDFIRE. (*without*) Heigh! Wake, snakes—June bugs are cumming.

MRS. WOLLOPE. (*jumping up*) He's here! Mary— Mary!

Mary runs in.

MRS. WOLLOPE. Where's my brother?[29]

MARY. Step'd out, ma'am, with Miss Caroline.

MRS. WOLLOPE. Step'd out? Then who's that coming up stairs.

MARY. The Reverend Mr. Dobbs!

MRS. WOLLOPE. The clergyman! Yah—I'm sacri-
ficed — help — murder! bigamy! (*Rings a handbell
violently and falls into a chair. Wildfire runs in on
one side, dragging with him a gentleman in black.*[30]
*Mrs. Freeman and Servants enter opposite picture.
Scene closes.*)

SCENE 2: *Room in a boarding house. Enter Percival
with a newspaper.*

PERCIVAL. (*reads*) "February 5th died suddenly at
the Hermitage near Swansea the right Honorable Lord
George Grandby—" Can this be possible? My rival an
impostor? Can he dare so great an insult to his country?
When I consider his conduct my doubts rise to conviction.
How shall I proceed? To denounce him on so slight a
proof might look like envy, yet to hazard the happiness
of her whom I love above all breathing beings is im-
possible. I will enclose this paper to her father. (*Sits
and writes.*)

Wildfire heard without.

WILDFIRE. Upstairs, is he? Never mind, I'll find him.

PERCIVAL. Ah, my Kentucky friend; like most un-
cultivated plants, a sound core with all his roughness of
exterior.

Enter Wildfire.

WILDFIRE. Ah, Percival, my boy, how goes it? What,
so I discovered last night that you are clinched in a love
match with my cousin Carry. Well, she's a peeler, ain't

she? But, I say, Percy, you must mind—hunt close upon the trail.

PERCIVAL. Ah, Colonel, I'm afraid I shall never run down the game.

WILDFIRE. What, why the little cretur hasn't dodged you? As we hunters say, won't she squat?

PERCIVAL. Why, to confess the truth, circumstances have recently transpired which involve me in some difficulty.

WILDFIRE. What! not out of ammunition — don't want money? If you do, I'm your man for five hundred or a thousand dollars. Draw upon *me*; I'll answer your drafts—draw like a horse.

PERCIVAL. I'm obliged to your generosity, but you mistake me. My difficulties are not pecuniary. To be candid with you, I am not a favorite with your aunt. You must have observed last night the preference she displayed towards my noble countryman.

WILDFIRE. Last night? No, I didn't see much of anything—I put too much brandy in my water. I was pretty particularly sprung.

PERCIVAL. Briefly, then—his Lordship is a suitor for your cousin's hand.

WILDFIRE. Oh, it's nothing but her vanity makes her listen to that Lord, and "Vanity, thy name is woman." So says Shakspeare, and warn't he a screamer?

PERCIVAL. But what adds to my uneasiness is my strong suspicion that he is not what he pretends to be.

WILDFIRE. What? Why, you don't think he is cheating, do you—as we say in Kaintuck, "playing possum"?

Theatre Royal, Dublin.

THE PUBLIC IS RESPECTFULLY INFORMED THAT

THE THEATRE WILL RE-OPEN
FOR THE SUMMER SEASON
This present TUESDAY, MAY 28, 1833,

ON WHICH OCCASION THE CELEBRATED

AMERICAN COMEDIAN
MR.
HACKETT

Who has performed with most triumphant success throughout the United States of America, and at the Theatres Royal Drury Lane and Covent Garden, and who is engaged

For Four Nights only,
Will make his first appearance in two Original Characters.

The Entertainments will commence with an alteration of Coleman's Comedy of

WHO WANTS A GUINEA
Or, A Yankee in England.

Torrent	...	Mr SHUTER, (in consequence of Mr RELLS'S illness.	
Heartly	...	Mr LAMBERT	Barford ... Mr CALCRAFT
Hogmore...Mr DUFF	Jonathan Oldskirt...Mr J. PENSON	Sir Larry Mac Murragh... Mr BARRY	
Andrew Bang ... Mr JOHNSON	Carrydot ... Mr STODHART	Henry ... Mr KING	

Solomon Swap, a Yankee in England .... **Mr. HACKETT,**
(His first appearance in this Kingdom.)

Fanny...Mrs PETTINGAL   Mrs Glastonbury... Miss BARRY   Amy...Miss BURGISS

A Pas de Deux by Master and Miss HARVEY.

After which (first time) a new Farce called the

KENTUCKIAN:
Or, A Trip to New York.

Colonel Nimrod Wildfire .... **Mr. HACKETT.**
Freeman, a New York Merchant...Mr SHUTER   Percival, an English Merchant.. Mr LAMBERT
Jenkins, under the assumed name of Lord Granby...Mr KING   Cæsar, a Free Black Waiter-Mr DUFF
Mrs Luminary, a Tourist and Speculator...Miss BARRY   Mrs Freeman...Mrs F. CONNOR
Caroline...Miss CHALMERS   Jarv...Mr LAMBERT   Waiting Maid...Miss BURGESS

The Performances will conclude with a new Indian Melodrama, in Two Acts, called the

Cherokee Chief:
Or, The Dogs of the Wreck.

IN WHICH

MR. CONY

WHO IS ENGAGED FOR A FEW NIGHTS ONLY, WILL INTRODUCE HIS CELEBRATED DOGS

HECTOR and BRUIN.

PLAYBILL *for the Dublin performance of "The Kentuckian." Reproduced from a copy in the Crawford Theatre Collection, Yale University Library.*

PERCIVAL. I must confess I have had cause.

WILDFIRE. Well, look here, Percival—I like an honest man let him come from what land he may and *perhaps* I like John Bull the best because we all come from one mother hen, tho' our brood was hatched this side of the water, but I hate a cheating possum, and if you are sure this Lord is a possum—

PERCIVAL. I have no proof upon the point. My doubts arise from a few words in a paper which I confess I can't understand.

WILDFIRE. Well, that's not my case. He has sent me a paper that I do (*Gives one to Percival.*) It's a beautiful piece of furniture—read it.

PERCIVAL. (*reads*) "Sir—Your presumptuous familiarity with me last night and your subsequent display of Kentucky civility towards a lady who has claimed my protection warrant me in demanding from you the satisfaction of a gentleman. You will let me know before tomorrow where a friend can wait upon you. Grandby." Why, Colonel, this certainly does look very like a challenge, but do you mean to fight him?

WILDFIRE. Distinctly. He'll find there's no mistake in me. I always go primed for such fun!

PERCIVAL. But, Colonel, you'll not be too hasty in this business.

WILDFIRE. Hasty? I'm always as cool as an Ingen, but if he wants to pick a quarrel with *me*, he'll stand a mighty sudden chance of being *used up*.

PERCIVAL. You, of course, allude to the treatment of a gentleman.

WILDFIRE. A gentleman? Oh, I'll put it to him *like* a *gentleman,* but if this had happened about ten years ago — when I was chock full of fun and fight — I wouldn't have minded going it in Old Mississippi style.

PERCIVAL. Some mode once peculiar to the wildness of the region?

WILDFIRE. Why, I'll tell you how it was. I was riding along the Mississippi one day when I came across a fellow floating down the stream sitting cock'd up in the starn of his boat fast asleep. Well, I hadn't had a fight for as much as ten days—felt as though I must kiver myself up in a salt bin to keep—"so wolfy" about the head and shoulders. So, says I, hullo, stranger, if you don't take keer your boat will run away wi' you. So he looked up at me "slantindickular," and I looked down on him "slanchwise." He took out a chaw of tobacco from his mouth and, says he, I don't value you tantamount to that, and then he flopp'd his wings and crowed like a cock. I ris up, shook my mane, crooked my neck, and neighed like a horse. Well, he run his boat foremost ashore. I stopped my waggon and set my triggers. Mister, says he, I'm the best man—if I ain't, I wish I may be tetotaciously exflunctified! I can whip my weight in wild cats and ride strait through a crab apple orchard on a flash of lightning—clear meat axe disposition! And what's more, I once back'd a bull off a bridge. Poh, says I, what do I keer for that? I can tote a steam boat up the Mississippi and over the Alleghany mountains. My father can whip the best man in old Kaintuck, and I can whip my father. When I'm good natured I weigh about a hundred and seventy, but when I'm mad, I weigh a *ton.* With that I fetched him the regular Ingen warwhoop. Out he jumped from his boat, and down I tumbled from my waggon—and, I say, we came together like two steam boats going sixty mile an hour. He was a pretty severe colt, but no part of a priming to such a feller as me. I put it to him mighty droll—tickled the varmint till he squealed like a young colt, bellowed "enough" and swore I was a "rip staver." Says I, *ain't* I a horse? Says he, stranger, you're a *beauty* anyhow, and if you'd stand for Congress I'd vote for you next *lection*. Says I, would you? My name's Nimrod Wildfire. Why, I'm the yaller flower of the forest. I'm all *brimstone but* the *head*, and that's *aky fortis*.

PERCIVAL. A renowned achievement. Well, Colonel, I feel it my duty before I leave New York to disclose the rumor I have heard to your uncle. Proceed in this affair as you think best, but remember, if you do meet his Lordship, it must be with the weapons of a gentleman. (*Exit.*)

WILDFIRE. A gentleman's weapons? Oh, of course, he means rifles. May be that Lord has heard of mine. She's a noisy varmint made of Powder house lightningrod steel and twisted like our Kentucky widow. She's got but one peeper, but if she blinks that at him, his head will hum like a hornet's nest—he'll see the stars dance in the day time. He'll come off as badly as a feller I once hit a sledge hammer lick over the head—a rale "sogdolloger." He disappeared altogether; all they could ever find of him was a little grease spot in one corner. (*Exit.*)

SCENE 3: *Park behind Mr. Freeman's house. Enter Jenkins followed by two men.*

JENKINS. Where have you placed the coach?

1ST MAN. At the end of the Park wall, your honor— just under the shade of that great oak.

JENKINS. Very well. In less than half an hour the female will leave the Park with me in that direction. Follow us to a convenient spot, and then you know your instructions. (*They go out. He comes forward.*) Caroline today informed me that her heart was filled with affection for another, but I also found out that it was filled with as much pride as affection. If, therefore, I can contrive to get her into my power for a few days, a respect to appearances must induce her to submit. Through her mother's influence I have engaged her for a walk, and here she comes—eh—her mother's with her. Zounds, here's a predicament—my plan's ruined!

Enter Mrs. Freeman and Caroline.

MRS. FREEMAN. My Lord, Caroline is fearful she has kept you waiting.

JENKINS. Time, madam, always seems long when I expect her presence. (Now to separate them—how to get away the old woman?)

MRS. FREEMAN. I regret to delay you longer, but, my Lord, I have a few words to say to you [in private] before you leave the Park.

JENKINS. In private—in private? My dear madam, will you walk this way? (*Handing her off.*) Bravo! Fortune still favors me.

CAROLINE. Why should I gratify a man I detest at the expense of an aching heart? Surely illness of mind is as important as a headache. I will return and for once incur the charge of hypocrisy. (*Exit.*)

Enter Mrs. Wollope.

MRS. WOLLOPE. Mr. Freeman has not yet come back from the city, and I am still in ignorance of the fate of my project. The attempt of that alligator colonel this morning has only more firmly convinced me of what I all along suspected—a design to smuggle [me] into the backwoods because I have come here to enlighten them. I fear an ambuscade in every bush and the signal for assault in each murmur of the wind. (*Opens the gate.*) All's quiet and lonely—not a soul in sight. Courage, Amelia,[31] do you shrink from danger? No, they shall see I have the spirit of a true ameliorator. (*Passes out of the gate.*)

Re-enter Jenkins.

JENKINS. Ha, there she glides. Bravo! she's mine! A lucky interruption of the old lady. She wished to warn me of her nephew, the Alligator Colonel, as my sister calls him.[32] Ha, ha! She little knows I have scared him back to his woods. I have seen nothing of him since I sent the challenge. No, no, I can imagine him on the back of a rough colt without saddle or bridle, belabouring the poor beast with a thick stick and fearing to turn his head lest he should perceive— (*Wildfire enters thro the gate in his hunter's dress with a rifle on each shoulder.*) Death and the devil!

WILDFIRE. Well, stranger, here I am.

JENKINS. Well, sir?

WILDFIRE. I got your letter, and you'll find there's no mistake about my being a gentleman.

JENKINS. (*aside*) Does he mean to apologize?

WILDFIRE. I say, stranger, you're a bran new pen, but perhaps I shall use you up to the stump.

JENKINS. Up to the stump? I don't understand you, sir.

WILDFIRE. You don't? (Why, he knows no more of English than a Winnebago squaw.) About this little *duel* business—you had better look to your spurs, or I shall cut your comb for you.

JENKINS. You mean to say, sir, you accept my challenge?

WILDFIRE. Yes, ready to blaze away like a fire in a prairie.

JENKINS. Very well. As you must be ignorant of the preliminaries we adopt in *civilized* society, you'll be good enough to name a friend, and mine shall wait upon him tomorrow morning.

WILDFIRE. Oh, no need of waiting till tomorrow morning; among my other trifles I should forget it, so we will have it on the spot.

JENKINS. On the spot?

WILDFIRE. Yes. Don't look wild—treat you like a gentleman.

JENKINS. But, sir, I can't fight now. I have an engagement.

WILDFIRE. Well, we'll have the engagement right off. Here, take your choice of these rifles. Either of them will do anything but talk.

JENKINS. Fight with rifles? Does the man take me for a buffalo? (*Aside.*)

WILDFIRE. I believe he's going to skulk. I must warm his blood a bit. A word in your ear: hang me, but I think you're a *possum*. If that don't make him fight, he's a trifling feller.

JENKINS. Here's a situation. I shall be murdered in cold blood, and if Caroline should have miss'd my myrmidons— (*Turning round with vehemence.*) My good sir, in one word I can't fight with you today.

WILDFIRE. Come, come, stranger. You have called me out, and if you think to get rid of me without exchanging a shot, you might as well try to scull a potash kettle up the falls of Niagara with a crowbar for an oar.

JENKINS. I'm caught in a pretty trap. (*Aside.*)

WILDFIRE. (*forcing the gun into his hand*) Now what should be the distance?

JENKINS. Why, I should say about half a mile.

WILDFIRE. What? Too far. Do you want me to *strain* my *rifle*? Twelve paces are as good as a million.

JENKINS. Twelve paces! Why, we might as well fight in a washing tub.

WILDFIRE. Come on, now, we'll stand back to back and each measure off six.

JENKINS. But, sir, these are not my weapons. Pistols are my weapons.

WILDFIRE. Pistols? Oh, nonsense. Good for nothing popguns that are sure to lodge the ball in you and wound your feelings. A rifle sends it clean through and thro.

JENKINS. Does he take one for a deal board?[33] But a rat will turn when driven to a corner. So, come on, sir. (*Retreating and levelling.*)

WILDFIRE. Stop! Look here, stranger. I'll bet you a hundred dollars that I put my bullet between your eyes without touching your nose. Now back to back and pace off, and when I count one, two, three, turn round and blaze away like a thunder cloud.

MRS. WOLLOPE. (*without*) Help, help! (*Cracking of a whip, &c.*)

JENKINS. Ah, Caroline is in their hands. It's neck or nothing. Now, sir. (*They prepare and are about to fire when they hear another shriek, and the coach comes on beyond the wall, its top just visible, containing Mrs. Wollope, who stretches out her head and arms in sight of the spectators—the driver in full view, lashing vigorously the horses, which are not seen.*)

MRS. WOLLOPE. Help, murder! Jenkins, they are carrying me to Kentucky!

JENKINS. My sister![34]

WILDFIRE. Hollo, what's the fun? (*Wheels round and levels his gun at the coach. Mrs. Wollope at the sight screams and disappears.*) Stop your steam for Kentucky there, driver! Come back, or I'll plug you like a watermelon. (*The coach goes off. Wildfire aims, and a crash is heard. The gate opens, and Mr. Freeman advances; Mrs. Freeman and Caroline enter from house.*)

FREEMAN. Nimrod, Mrs. Wollope is in safety, and the perpetrator of this outrage stands before you. But how is this? Have you been fighting? I would, sir, that you could display this courage in a good cause.

JENKINS. Mr. Freeman—

FREEMAN. Sir, I have this day received the amplest evidence that you are not entitled to the name you bear.

WILDFIRE. There, I know'd he was a possum!

FREEMAN. I have cause also to suspect that this conduct towards my guest was intended for my daughter. As your designs are exposed, you will spare us the further uneasiness of your presence.

JENKINS. Mr. Freeman, as I cannot deny, I shall not attempt to defend my intentions, but permit me—

WILDFIRE. Stop, stranger. Do you know I can out eat any man in this country?

JENKINS. Well, sir?

WILDFIRE. So if you'll wait until I've untied my neck-cloth—

JENKINS. What then?

WILDFIRE. I'll swallow you whole. (*Exit Jenkins.*)

Enter Percival and Mrs. Wollope.

MRS. WOLLOPE. Another outrage! Is the whole continent in arms against me?

FREEMAN. No, madam, but I regret to inform you, madam, that our inhabitants are unfavourable to your design.

MRS. WOLLOPE. Indeed!

FREEMAN. It is their opinion that as refinement in all countries has been the result of wealth and leisure, America must provide for her wants before she can be in a condition to welcome those who would increase her luxuries.

MRS. WOLLOPE. Then you reject my offers. You despise my sympathy.[35] You are so infatuated that you would scruple a paltry 500 dollars for instruction. But I have my remedy—I have made my observations.[36] I'll return with them to England; I'll give them to the world, and posterity shall judge between us. (*Exit.*)

WILDFIRE. I say, uncle Peter, ain't she a screamer?

FREEMAN. Percival, if you and Caroline wish to be united, you have my consent; we ask but to be looked at like other people, not with the eye of prejudice or interest, but of candor. We have our evil with our good, but we feel that there are affinities between the Briton and American which should quench the petty fires of dissension and establish on the basis of their mutual freedom the glorious altar of fraternity.[37]

PERCIVAL. What say you, Colonel?

WILDFIRE. Why, as there seems to be a talk about countries, I think you had all better pack up your plunder and tote off to Kaintuck. I'll divide all my land among you on the Big Muddy and the Little Muddy free gratis for nothing, and look here, the ground's so rich there that if you but plant a crowbar over night *perhaps* it will sprout tenpenny nails afore mornin'. (*Coming forward.*) Look here, ladies and gentlemen, strangers, I know I'm a pretty hard sample of a white man, but I don't want to skeer nobody; and as you see I'm in want of a little more genteel education, I hope I may be indulged occasionally in a "trip to New York."

END.

Appendix

THE B-TEXT

The B-text may be reconstructed by making the following changes in the passages indicated in the A-text.

[1] Substitute "Mrs. Luminary" for "Mrs. Wollope" here and throughout the play.

[2] Omit "this is not the place to discuss the merits of an European institution."

[3] Omit "If the result has been the people's happiness."

[4] Omit "to observe our domestic manners."

[5] Substitute "nation" for "national manners."

[6] Omit "What the causes of this row in the south Carolina?"

[7] Omit "on our domestic manners."

[8] Omit "Ever since the death of her husband, honest Frank Wollope," and substitute "friend" for "sister."

[9] Omit "To ameliorate the barbarism of manners in America has been the ruling wish of my life; my husband, the only obstacle to its fulfillment, by his death has provided me with the means, and."

[10] Omit "the state of manners of."

[11] Substitute "A Mr. Jenkins" for "My brother."

[12] Omit "But I see the aim of this. This has all been concerted to give me a favourable impression of their country."

[13] Omit "Amelia" and "for heaven's sake."

[14] Omit " 'Domestic Manners of the Americans' " and "to be illustrated with a sketch of him in his favorite position, rocking in a chair with his legs out of the window."

[15] Omit "of manners."

[16] Substitute "Mr. Jenkins" for "My brother."

¹⁷ Substitute "a" for "another."

¹⁸ Omit "Good heavens."

¹⁹ Omit "I was warned of the total want of probity of these people."

²⁰ Substitute "them" for "their manners."

²¹ Substitute "Mrs. Luminary" for "Amelia."

²² Substitute "Is it you?" for "It's well you've come at last, sir."

²³ Substitute "Mrs. Luminary" for "sister."

²⁴ Substitute "friend" for "brother."

²⁵ Substitute "Mrs. Luminary" for "Amelia."

²⁶ Omit "by heaven."

²⁷ Substitute "Mrs. Luminary" for "Amelia."

²⁸ Omit "and yet if I fear the barbarisms of these people, how shall I ever overcome them? I'll look at it less seriously. Stay, it would make a feature in my Journal. Let me see—yes, under this head: 'Anecdote of the Alligator Colonel'—'mode of marrying in a whirlwind.' Ha, ha, ha!"

²⁹ Substitute "Mr. Jenkins" for "my brother."

³⁰ Omit "*dragging with him a gentleman in black.*"

³¹ Substitute "Mrs. Luminary" for "Amelia."

³² Substitute "one" for "me" and "the Kentuckian" for "the Alligator Colonel, as my sister calls him."

³³ In the A-text this sentence was preceded by what from the context seems to have been an expletive. The word was marked over so well by the B-text adapter that it could not be reconstructed.

³⁴ Substitute "Mrs. Luminary!" for "My sister!"

³⁵ Omit "You despise my sympathy."

³⁶ Omit "I have my remedy."

³⁷ Omit "not with the eye of prejudice or interest, but of candor. We have our evil with our good, but we feel that."